# SNOOPY

( features as )

# Master of Disguise

**Charles M. Schulz**

PEANUTS is a registered trademark of
United Feature Syndicate, Inc.
Based on the PEANUTS® comic strip
by Charles M. Schulz.

Originally published in 1988 as
'Snoopy Stars as the The Great Pretender'.
This edition published in 2002 by Ravette Publishing.

---

Printed and bound in Great Britain
for Ravette Publishing Limited,
Unit 3, Tristar Centre,
Star Road, Partridge Green,
West Sussex  RH13 8RA
by Cox & Wyman, Berkshire.

ISBN: 1 84161 161 1

4-2

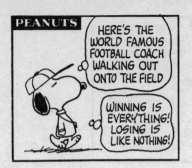

PEANUTS

HERE'S THE WORLD FAMOUS FOOTBALL COACH WALKING OUT ONTO THE FIELD

WINNING IS EVERYTHING! LOSING IS LIKE NOTHING!

THIS YEAR WE'RE GOING TO STRESS PHYSICAL CONDITIONING.. LOTS OF PUSH-UPS AND PLENTY OF RUNNING...

9-2

?

WOODSTOCK ALWAYS HAS TROUBLE WITH PUSH-UPS

I SHOULD THINK YOU'D GET BORED JUST SITTING ON A DOGHOUSE ALL DAY..

ON THE CONTRARY..

WHO COULD GET BORED FLYING THE STAR SHIP "ENTERPRISE"?

© 1988 United Feature Syndicate, Inc. 1-18

YOU KNOW WHAT'S A BAD SIGN?

WHEN YOU MEET YOUR DOCTOR IN THE HALLWAY OF THE HOSPITAL, AND HE DOESN'T RECOGNIZE YOU..

© 1979 United Feature Syndicate, Inc.

HERE'S THE WORLD FAMOUS SURVEYOR PREPARING A LAND DESCRIPTION...

"RICHARD ROE...
N 81° 02' W 184.32 ft.
S 61° 47' W 187.15 ft."

"JOHN DOE...HMM....
N 19° 45' W 285.62 ft."

6-20  © 1979 United Feature Syndicate, Inc.

EXCUSE ME..I THINK YOU'RE STANDING ON MAIN STREET

RING!

HAVEN'T YOU READ IN THE OLD TESTAMENT HOW KING DAVID GOT INTO TROUBLE FOR TAKING A CENSUS?

4-3

© 1980 United Feature Syndicate, Inc.

I WAS JUST SUPPOSED TO ASK THEM HOW MANY BATHTUBS THEY HAVE..

WHEN YOU GO SOME PLACE NICE, YOU SHOULD ALWAYS SHINE YOUR FEET!

© 1983 United Feature Syndicate, Inc.  8-26

## Other PEANUTS titles published by Ravette ...

| Pocket Books | ISBN | Price |
|---|---|---|
| Man's Best Friend | 1 84161 066 6 | £2.99 |
| Master of the Fairways | 1 84161 067 4 | £2.99 |
| The Fearless Leader | 1 84161 104 2 | £2.99 |
| The Fitness Fanatic | 1 84161 029 1 | £2.99 |
| The Flying Ace | 1 84161 027 5 | £2.99 |
| The Great Entertainer | 1 84161 160 3 | £2.99 |
| The Great Philosopher | 1 84161 064 X | £2.99 |
| The Legal Beagle | 1 84161 065 8 | £2.99 |
| The Literary Ace | 1 84161 026 7 | £2.99 |
| The Master Chef | 1 84161 107 7 | £2.99 |
| The Matchmaker | 1 84161 028 3 | £2.99 |
| The Music Lover | 1 84161 106 9 | £2.99 |
| The Sportsman | 1 84161 105 0 | £2.99 |
| The Tennis Ace | 1 84161 162 X | £2.99 |
| The Winter Wonder Dog | 1 84161 163 8 | £2.99 |

| Little Books | ISBN | Price |
|---|---|---|
| Charlie Brown - Friendship | 1 84161 156 5 | £2.50 |
| Charlie Brown - Wisdom | 1 84161 099 2 | £2.50 |
| Educating Peanuts | 1 84161 158 1 | £2.50 |
| Lucy - Advice | 1 84161 101 8 | £2.50 |
| Peanuts - Life | 1 84161 157 3 | £2.50 |
| Peppermint Patty - Blunders | 1 84161 102 6 | £2.50 |
| Snoopy - Laughter | 1 84161 100 X | £2.50 |
| Snoopy - Style | 1 84161 155 7 | £2.50 |

| Colour Landscapes | ISBN | Price |
|---|---|---|
| Passion for Peanuts | 1 84161 153 0 | £4.50 |
| Snoopy Unleashed | 1 84161 154 9 | £4.50 |

| Miscellaneous | ISBN | Price |
|---|---|---|
| Peanuts Anniversary Treasury | 1 84161 021 6 | £9.99 |
| Peanuts Treasury | 1 84161 043 7 | £9.99 |
| You Really Don't Look 50 Charlie Brown | 1 84161 020 8 | £7.99 |

| Snoopy's Laughter and Learning | ISBN | Price |
|---|---|---|
| Book 1 - Read with Snoopy | 1 84161 016 X | £2.50 |
| Book 2 - Write with Snoopy | 1 84161 017 8 | £2.50 |
| Book 3 - Count with Snoopy | 1 84161 018 6 | £2.50 |
| Book 4 - Colour with Snoopy | 1 84161 019 4 | £2.50 |

All PEANUTS books are available at your local bookshop or from the publisher at the address below. Just tick the titles required and send the form with your payment to:-

RAVETTE PUBLISHING, Unit 3, Tristar Centre, Star Road, Partridge Green, West Sussex RH13 8RA

Prices and availability are subject to change without prior notice.

Please enclose a cheque or postal order made payable to **Ravette Publishing** to the value of the cover price of the book and allow the following for UK postage and packing:-

55p for the first book + 30p for each additional book, except *You Really Don't Look 50 Charlie Brown* when please add £1.50 p&p per copy and the two *Treasuries* when please add £2.50 p&p per book.

Name .................................................................................................................

Address .................................................................................................................

.................................................................................................................

.................................................................................................................